the m glee
best of season one

CW00341778

Wise Publications
part of The Music Sales Group
London / New York / Paris / Sydney / Copenhagen /
Berlin / Madrid / Hong Kong / Tokyo

Published by
Wise Publications
14-15 Berners Street, London W1T 3LJ, UK.

Exclusive distributors:
Music Sales Limited
Distribution Centre,
Newmarket Road, Bury St Edmunds, Suffolk, IP33 3YB, UK.
Music Sales Pty Limited
20 Resolution Drive, Caringbah, NSW 2229, Australia.

Order No. AM1002771
ISBN 978-1-84938-965-5

This book © Copyright 2011 Wise Publications,
a division of Music Sales Limited.

Edited by Jenni Wheeler.

Printed in the EU.

www.musicsales.com

Your Guarantee of Quality

As publishers, we strive to produce every book to the highest
commercial standards. The music has been freshly engraved and
the book has been carefully designed to minimise awkward page
turns and to make playing from it a real pleasure.

Particular care has been given to specifying acid-free, neutral-sized
paper made from pulps which have not been elemental chlorine bleached.

This pulp is from farmed sustainable forests and was
produced with special regard for the environment.

Throughout, the printing and binding have been planned to ensure a sturdy,
attractive publication which should give years of enjoyment.

If your copy fails to meet our high standards, please inform us
and we will gladly replace it.

www.musicsales.com

Rehab

Words & Music by Amy Winehouse

know it don't come in a shot glass.____ They

tried to make me go to re - hab____ but I said____ no, no, no.

Yes,____ I've been black but when____ I come back you'll____

know, know, know. I ain't got the time,____

and if my dad-dy thinks_ I'm fine._____ They

tried to make me go to re - hab_ but I won't_ go, go, go.

The man said "Why do you think_ you here?"___ (Why do you think___ you here?)___

I say "I got no i - dea."_____ "I'm

Don't Stop Believin'

Words & Music by Steve Perry, Neal Schon
& Jonathan Cain

1. Just a small town girl,— liv - ing in a
3. Work - ing hard to get my fill.— Ev - 'ry - bod - y

2. A sing-er in a smo-key room,— the smell of wine— and cheap per-fume.—

For a smile— they can share the night. It goes on and on— and on— and on.

Take A Bow

Words & Music by Mikkel Eriksen, Tor Erik Hermansen
& Shaffer Smith

Mercy

Words & Music by Duffy & Stephen Booker

Somebody To Love

Words & Music by Freddie Mercury

try and I try and I try,_____ but ev - 'ry-bod - y wants to put me down, they

say__ I'm go - in' cra - zy._____ They say I got a lot of wa-ter in my brain,_____ got__

__ no com-mon sense.__ I got no - bod-y left to be - lieve._____ Yeah,__ yeah,__ yeah,__ yeah.__

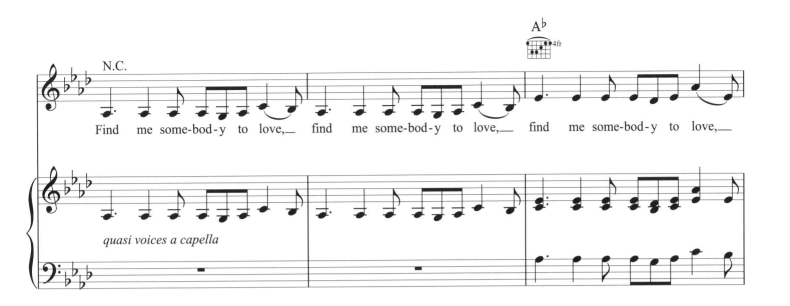

Find me some-bod-y to love,___ find me some-bod-y to love,___ find me some-bod-y to love,

quasi voices a capella

find me some-bod - y to love,___ find me some-bod - y to love,___

find me some-bod - y to love,___ find me some-bod-y to love,___

find me some-bod-y to love._____ Find me some-bod-y to love,___

find me some-bod-y to love.____ Some-bod-y, some-bod-y, some-bod-y, some-bod-y,

some-bod-y, find me some-bod-y, find me some-bod-y to love. Can

A tempo

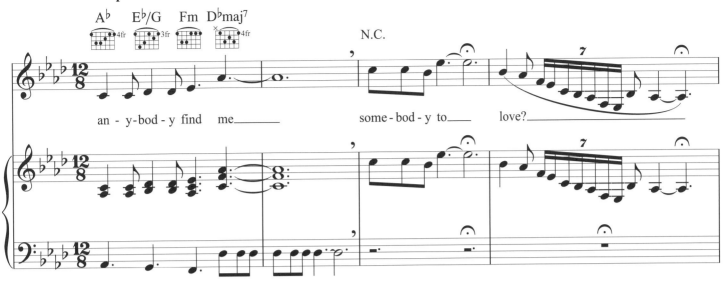

an - y-bod - y find me_____ some-bod - y to_____ love?_____

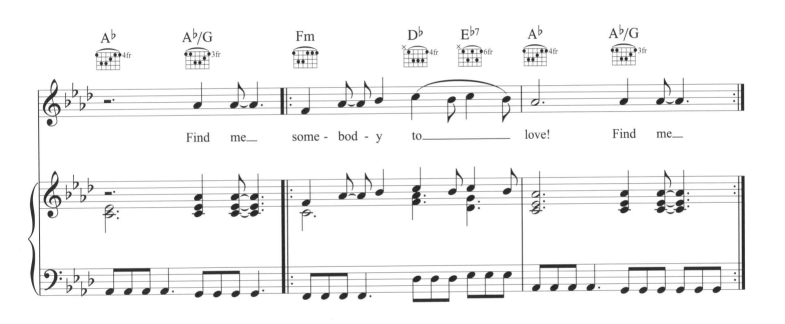

Find me_ some - bod - y to_____ love! Find me_

some - bod - y to_____ love! Find me, find me, find me, find me.

Halo / Walking On Sunshine

'Halo' Words & Music by Ryan Tedder, Beyoncé Knowles & Evan Kidd Bogart
'Walking On Sunshine' Words & Music by Kimberley Rew

ha - lo, ha - lo. I can see your ha - lo, and don't it feel_ good!_

I used to think may - be you loved_ me; now, ba - by I'm sure._

And I just can't wait_ till the day_ when you knock_ on my door._

Keep Holding On

Words & Music by Avril Lavigne & Lukasz Gottwald

1. You're not a-lone. To-geth-er we stand. I'll be by your
2. So far a-way, I wish you were here. Be-fore it's too

side, you know I'll take your hand. When it gets cold and it feels like the end,
late, this could all dis-ap - pear. Be-fore the doors close and it comes to an end,

there's no place to go___ you know I won't give___ in. No, I won't give

with you by my side___ I will fight and de- fend. I'll fight and de-

in.___ Keep hold - ing

-fend.___

on___ 'cause you know we'll make it through, we'll make it through. Just

stay___ strong___ 'cause you know I'm here for you, I'm here for you.

46

Sweet Caroline

Words & Music by Neil Diamond

Original key C# major

Moderately, very steady

1. Where it be - gan,___

I can't be - gin to know - in'.

But then I know it's grow - in' strong.

Was-n't the spring___ and spring be - came the sum - mer.___

Who'd have be - lieved___ you'd come a - long?

1. Hands,___ touch- in' hands,___
Warm,___ touch- in' warm,___

hurt - in' runs off my shoul - der. How can I hurt,—

when hold - ing you?

D.S. al Coda

Coda

Sweet Car - o - line,___ good times nev - er seemed so

good._____ I've been in - clined___

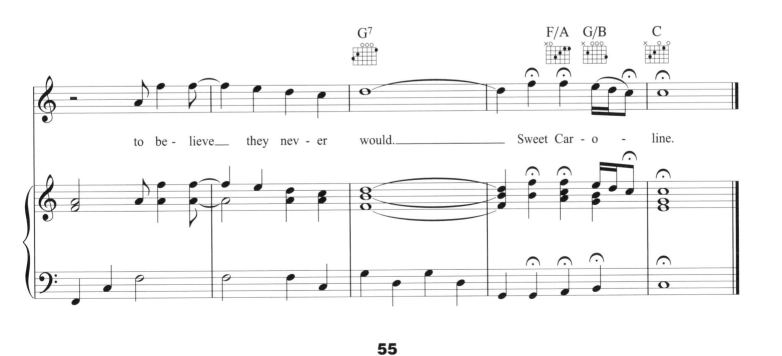

to be - lieve___ they nev - er would._____ Sweet Car - o - line.

Defying Gravity

Words & Music by Stephen Schwartz

1. Some-thing has changed with-in me, some-thing is not the same.
2. I'm through ac-cept-ing lim-its 'cause some-one says they're so.

I'm through with play-ing by the rules of some-one else-'s game.
Some things I can-not change but till I try I'll nev-er know.

True Colors

Words & Music by Billy Steinberg & Tom Kelly

Guitar

like a rain - - bow.

1.

2. Show me a

Oh,

oh.

I can't re-mem-ber when I last saw you laugh. If

To Coda ⊕

61

Don't Stand So Close To Me / Young Girl

'Don't Stand So Close To Me' Words & Music by Sting
'Young Girl' Words & Music by Jerry Fuller

With all the charms___ of_ a wom - an___ (Ooh.)___

you've kept the se - cret___ of your youth. (Ah.)___

Book mark - ing she's so close now, this girl is half his age.___

Don't stand, don't stand so, don't stand so

'Cause I'm a-fraid___ you'll go too far..._____

Don't stand,   don't stand so,   don't stand so close to me.___

Don't stand,   don't stand so,   don't stand so close to me.___

Young girl___ you're out of your mind.___   Your love for me is way out of line.___ Bet-ter run___

My Life Would Suck Without You

Words & Music by Max Martin, Lukasz Gottwald & Claude Kelly

1. Guess this means you're sor - ry, you're stand - ing at my door.
2. May - be I was stu - pid for tell - ing you good - bye.

'Cause we be-long_

to - geth - - - er now,_____ yeah,_

Gives You Hell

Words & Music by Tyson Ritter & Nick Wheeler

-ing. When you see my face hope it gives you hell, hope it gives you

hell. When you walk my way hope it gives you hell, hope it gives you___

___ hell. If you find a man___ that's worth a damn___ and treats you

well then he's a fool,___ you're just as well. Hope it gives you___

To Coda

79

hell.   If you find   a man   that's worth a damn   and treats you

well   then he's a fool,   you're just as well. Hope it gives you

A

hell.   When you see my   face hope it gives you hell, hope it gives you

D   **F♯m**   **E**

_ hell.   When you walk my   way hope it gives you hell, hope it gives you_

Like A Prayer

Words & Music by Madonna & Pat Leonard

Jessie's Girl

Words & Music by Rick Springfield

Total Eclipse Of The Heart

Words & Music by Jim Steinman

I Dreamed A Dream

Music by Claude-Michel Schönberg
Original Lyrics by Alain Boublil & Jean-Marc Natel
English Lyrics by Herbert Kretzmer

1. I dreamed a dream in time gone by, when hope was high and life worth
2. Then I was young and un - a - fraid, when dreams were made and used and

liv - ing.____ I dreamed that love would nev - er die,
wast - ed.____ There was no ran - som to be paid;

4. And still I dreamed he'd come to me, that we would live the years to-

-geth - er. _____ But there are dreams that can - not

be, and there are storms we can - not weath-er. _____

I had a dream my life would be

so diff-'rent from this hell I'm liv-ing;___ so diff-'rent now from what it

seemed. Now life has killed the dream I

dreamed.

Poker Face

Words & Music by Stefani Germanotta & Nadir Khayat

Over The Rainbow

Words by E.Y. Harburg
Music by Harold Arlen

123456789